MV £5.00

This book is to be retur...
the last date s...

2

BRITAIN'S OLD METAL MINES - a pictorial survey

BRITAIN'S OLD
METAL MINES

A PICTORIAL SURVEY

R. H. BIRD

D. BRADFORD BARTON LTD

Frontispiece An aerial photograph of Ubley Warren, in the Mendips. This shows a good example of "gruffy" ground, pock-marked with shaft hollows and workings on the backs of the veins. Charterhouse minery occupies the centre and the black area at the valley head is the supply reservoir used for dressing operations and for driving the water wheels. The circular earthwork at the top left hand side is the remains of a Roman mining settlement.   [*Crown copyright reserved*]   *N.G.R. ST 505555.*

© *copyright D. Bradford Barton Ltd & R. H. Bird 1974*

printed in Great Britain by H. E. Warne Ltd, London and St. Austell

for the publishers

D. BRADFORD BARTON LTD · **Trethellan House** · **Truro** · **Cornwall** · **England**

introduction

The great mineral wealth of Britain has resulted in myriads of mining sites, including many thousands of miles of hidden levels and workings, a large number of which are flooded and inaccessible. Mining has been taking place since the time of the Roman conquest until the present day, and of the several thousand sites that exist today, only a mere fraction can be recorded by the camera. A large number of them are however not worth recording, being perhaps merely an isolated mound in the corner of a field or a "run-in" shaft hollow.

The earlier workings of Roman or medieval time were frequently destroyed by later mining activity and only occasionally can traces of them be found. The dating of these workings, above or below ground, is difficult; frequently any unusual level, trench or tool which comes to light is indiscriminately attributed to the Romans. With few exceptions, therefore, the majority of interesting remains of non-ferrous metal mining which can be seen today date from the seventeenth to the twentieth centuries.

Some areas such as South-West England and the mid-Pennines are well endowed with interesting mining sites which, because of the magnitude of mining activity in those areas, coupled with the absence of large scale industrial and urban development, have been spared from the ubiquitous bulldozer.

In the last decade, there has been considerable interest shown in Industrial Archaeology, of which metal mining is, of course, a small branch. It is heartening to reflect that each year sees one or more historic mining sites added to the growing list of buildings and areas covered by preservation orders.

With an estimated 20 million tons of fluorspar reserves in Derbyshire and 5 million tons in the Northern Pennines, coupled with the fact that, in the opinion of many mining geologists, there remains more ore in Cornwall than has ever been extracted, it is probable that we are about to witness a revival in British non-ferrous mining. Whilst of great benefit to the economy of the country as a whole, this would cause a number of interesting remains to disappear. Some form of visible record is necessary for future generations. One of the aims of this book, therefore, is put on record a number of these sites and to encourage others to do likewise. After all, it is largely due to the efforts of contemporary individuals who made a record of events around them, that history is built up today.

The author has been recording mining areas for a number of years but the majority of the illustrations in this volume are taken relatively recently. Even so, the photographer's art suffers in much the same way as that of the cartographer, in that as time elapses the photographs can never be entirely in accordance with present-day conditions. An engine-house photographed today may have partly collapsed a short time later—improbable, knowing the strength of engine-houses, but nevertheless a possibility.

Various books devoted to the history of metal mining give the approximate locations of the sites concerned, but frequently Ordnance Survey grid references are omitted. These can be very helpful when one is engaged in field work and can save many wasted hours. For this reason, a six figure grid reference beneath each illustration is given as a guide to those readers who desire to visit the location.

Photographs taken below ground are included in this volume, for without them it would be incomplete, since many classical remains are only to be found there. This often requires arduous underground trips, not to be lightly attempted. Proper equipment and a knowledge of the hazards likely to be encountered are a basic requirement. Anyone lacking these essentials should contact a local caving club or similar body and should certainly not attempt to go underground alone. Surface exploration can have its attendant dangers also. Even to peer down an open shaft can be risky, owing to age making the collar liable to sudden collapse. Such shafts should be approached with great caution and are best viewed lying prone, thus giving maximum stability to one's person. A final word on safety. Frequently open shafts are ringed with barbed wire or other forms of protection and to climb these often results both in personal danger and the weakening of the wire. Gaps appear through which young children and animals can pass, a thing obviously to be prevented.

Richard Bird ARPS

South Anston,
Sheffield

acknowledgements

I should like to express my thanks to the following persons and organisations whose help in the compilation of this book has been greatly appreciated. To the Leadhills & Wanlockhead Mines Research Group for photographs and information pertaining to that area; to Mr D. Bick of Gloucester for the photograph on page 42; to the Derbyshire Caving Club for the photographs on page 100; to the Ministry of Defence (Air Force Department) for permission to reproduce the aerial photograph on page 2; to Miss A. Blockley, Librarian of the Brown Firth Research Laboratories for help in locating valuable reference sources; to Mr H. E. Bird and Mrs A. Lee for proof-reading and typing assistance respectively; to the Northern Cavern and Mines Research Society for much general assistance; to my publisher, Mr D. B. Barton not only for allowing me to use his photographs and information on various Eire mines but also for his general encouragement; and finally to my wife Hilary for her help and long sufferance in accompanying me on countless mining trips both above and below ground.

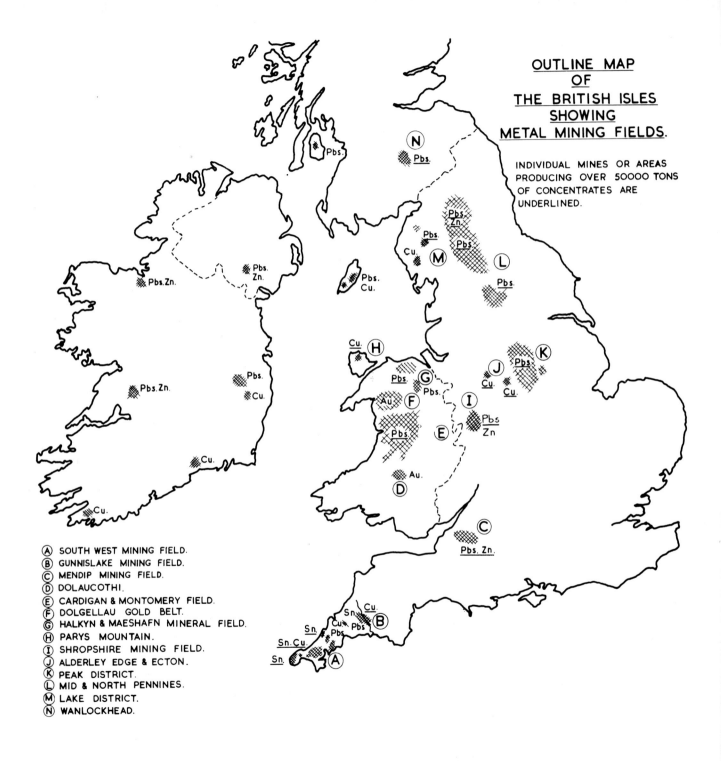

OUTLINE MAP
OF
THE BRITISH ISLES
SHOWING
METAL MINING FIELDS.

INDIVIDUAL MINES OR AREAS
PRODUCING OVER 50000 TONS
OF CONCENTRATES ARE
UNDERLINED.

(A) SOUTH WEST MINING FIELD.
(B) GUNNISLAKE MINING FIELD.
(C) MENDIP MINING FIELD.
(D) DOLAUCOTHI.
(E) CARDIGAN & MONTOMERY FIELD.
(F) DOLGELLAU GOLD BELT.
(G) HALKYN & MAESHAFN MINERAL FIELD.
(H) PARYS MOUNTAIN.
(I) SHROPSHIRE MINING FIELD.
(J) ALDERLEY EDGE & ECTON.
(K) PEAK DISTRICT.
(L) MID & NORTH PENNINES.
(M) LAKE DISTRICT.
(N) WANLOCKHEAD.

South-West England

South-West England was once the world's most important mining field for copper and tin, a position which it held until large discoveries of those metals overseas eclipsed the area in the mid-nineteenth century. Although thus displaced from its premier position, the industry struggled on with varying fortunes until the present day, when it still remains a viable field for future development.

The area is essentially a deep mining field brought into being by the following in depth of the tin and copper lodes which had previously been worked out on the surface by the "old men", as the miners of former times were known. These old men's workings are a conspicuous feature of the coastal area, particularly around Perranporth, where the cliffs resemble a Gruyere cheese in being a veritable labyrinth of tunnels and workings.

With only primitive pumps available at the time, lodes could not be followed much below the water table and, therefore, had to be abandoned until the advent of steam pumping engines. These engines, utilising huge cast-iron beams, were housed in equally substantial buildings situated beside the main or engine shaft of the mine. Today they remain a familiar feature of the Cornish landscape, largely roofless and in varying stages of decay. Usually they are found with chimney stacks built as an integral part of the house, although at certain mines, East Wheal Rose, for example, the stack is sited some distance away.

Perhaps the mines found on the Atlantic seaboard are the most impressive, particularly those at the extreme western end of the Duchy, in West Penwith. Two notable ones here are Botallack and Levant, the former having two engine-houses on precipitous cliffs.

Not all engine-houses are alike and occasionally one comes across rather squat-like structures bearing little resemblance to the typical form. These houses were probably built for inverted or horizontal types of engines which did not require strong, high walls on which to rest the beam. A fine example of such a house can be found on the South Frances section of Basset Mines near Redruth. The circular shaft here is also an unusual feature, as most engine shafts were rectangular in section. Again, the ladder road and hauling shafts found in the disturbed tracts of ground of the Cornish mining regions differ in structure from elsewhere in the country. Today they resemble bomb craters contained within rough, circular stone walls with no distinct collar, the edges funnelling into the shaft, thus making approach impossible. Engine shafts in use at a later period often have concrete collars however, to provide a solid foundation for balance bobs, shears and capstan gear.

Adits are a feature frequently seen in the mining areas, particularly on the cliffs. These drainage tunnels were driven from the coast or other low ground to provide drainage. Where steam engines were used, water pumped from the workings was discharged into the adit instead of lifting it to grass. The driving of these adits was also a useful method of prospecting untested ground and often resulted in the discovery of valuable ore deposits, some of which were later worked with great success.

Subsequent treatment of the ore required the considerable use of machinery and in tin mining particularly this needed crushing or stamping to a fine sand to release the tinstuff. The stamping was done by batteries of iron-shod stamps which were raised by lifters attached to a revolving shaft. This shaft was turned by a rotative steam engine or a water-wheel. After stamping, the tinstuff was separated from the waste in buddles and other gravity devices. All this activity required considerable space together with a source of water and each mine occupied an area for the dressing of its output. On a large sett containing many mines owned by a single group of adventurers, the dressing of the ore was often done on a common floor, the remains of which can often be seen, for example, those at the Basset Mines, where a 'communal' policy was adopted. At Blue Hills Mine in Trevellas Coombe, St. Agnes, the remains of the dressing floor, worked almost entirely by water power, can be traced extending from the mine down to the seashore.

Some notable exhibits which have been preserved (mainly by the Cornish Engines Preservation Society) include a whim (or winding) engine at Pool and the pumping engine at Taylor's shaft, the pumping engine at South Crofty mine nearby and the whim engine at Levant Mine, St. Just. In addition to these, a fine collection of working models can be seen at Holman's Museum at Camborne, together with a small beam pumping engine from the china clay pits at Rostowrack. Further east, on the southern extremities of Bodmin Moor, near Liskeard, is a tract of heavily mineralised copper ground which was worked at Caradon Hill by a number of mines whose gaunt ruins remain today. To the north, near the Cheesewring, lie the remains of Phoenix United Mines. Such was the importance of the area, that the Liskeard & Caradon Railway was specially constructed to carry ore to the coast at Looe for shipment to the South Wales smelters.

The River Tamar is the county boundary between Cornwall and Devon and in the district around Gunnislake many interesting mining features remain. A remarkable feature of this area is the heavy growth of ivy, which seems to cling to any disused building—the chimney stacks of the engine houses, in particular, often have the appearance of huge woolly pipe cleaners!

A wide range of minerals have been mined here, including copper, tin, lead, barytes, silver, wolfram and molybdenite. In particular, across the river in the county of Devon was the site of the extremely rich Devon Great Consols which, between the years 1845 and 1903, produced over 742,000 tons of $6\frac{1}{2}$ per cent copper ore. Unfortunately for those interested in old mines the site has since been reclaimed and afforested, so that little of the old workings can be seen today. However, a magnificently engineered water leat can still be traced, together with such items as water-wheel pits and the remains of dressing floors.

Further south and connected with Devon Great Consols by a

railway, was the port of Morwellham. Here was the termination of the Tavistock Canal, connected to Morwellham via an inclined tramway. The canal which pierced Morwell Down in a mile long tunnel, was an important additional link for mineral traffic to the port and in fact, the tunnel was itself utilised as a copper mine, a lode being discovered during its construction. Morwellham, with its quay, limekilns, canal terminus and inclines, is now in the hands of a Trust which ensures its preservation for all time.

Dartmoor has, for generations, been the home of tin streamers who worked alluvial tin on the moor. This tin was smelted in blowing houses, crude structures housing a furnace of moorstone and using charcoal as a fuel. Several of these blowing houses remain today and granite moulds used in casting of the molten tin are often found.

The Geological Survey of Great Britain, published in 1956, lists over 1500 mines in South-West England but this does not include the many sites of great historical interest such as dressing floors, arsenic works, railways and canals which were connected with the once extensive mining industry here. This will give the reader some indication of the extent of mining locations which may be visited today, of which only a few can be included within this volume.

The buildings of Levant Mine stand at the head of Levant Zawn, a large indentation in the cliffs where the softer lode material has been eroded. Levant is probably Cornwall's most famous tin mine and has, like many mines on the coast, been worked below the sea bed. The engine-house on the left contains a whim engine built in 1840 and is the oldest engine remaining in Cornwall. The one on the right contained the pumping engine which worked through the adjacent 290-fathom shaft. The head frame in the centre marks the position of the Skip shaft, also sunk to the 290 level, the former still being used as a service shaft in conjunction with mining activities of the nearby Geevor Mine.

N.G.R. SW 368345.

The huge rusted drum of the Levant whim. This engine drew skips of ore from the Skip shaft. The cylinder, valve gear and flywheel were renewed on this engine about 1862 after an accident which damaged the original components. The whim is now in the care of the Cornish Engines Preservation Society. *N.G.R. SW 368345.*

The engine-house at Higher Levant is situated some distance from the shaft which lies beneath the concrete cap in the foreground. The house contained a whim engine, the flywheel and drum being located between the masonry foundations at the front of the house. The headframe over the shaft was the last example of its kind to survive in the county and was dismantled about 1920. The site is unusual in that access to the shaft collar is reached by climbing a flight of steps through a tunnel from the road. *N.G.R. SW 369342.*

In former times the miner was required to climb ladders to and from his place of work which, in deep mines, was both exhausting and time consuming. However, in the mid nineteenth century the man-engine was developed. This utilised reciprocating rods hung in the shaft on to which sollars or platforms were attached. By stepping alternately from one platform to another, the miner was either lifted or lowered in the shaft at each stroke of the rod. Such a man engine, extending down to the 266 fathom level, was in use at Levant in 1919 when a fracture occurred at the angle bob at the shaft top. As safety catches were fitted to the rods they did not fall the whole way to the bottom but the men near the surface, where the catches failed to hold, were precipitated to their deaths. In all 31 miners lost their lives. The illustration shows the ruined engine house and boiler room of the man engine.

N.G.R. SW 368344.

The spectacular ruins of Botallack Mine seen from above at the site of Crowns Engine shaft which was sunk to the 135 fathom level. Due to the shortage of space where the engine-house is built, the stack has been incorporated inside the building which gives it a somewhat unusual appearance.

N.G.R. SW 362337.

A general view of the Crowns Section of Botallack Mine. A writer stated in 1822 that: "This mine was wrought under the sea beyond the memory of any person now living". It experienced a very successful career and in its heyday employed no less than 500 persons, had a total of eleven engines at work and has also been visited by Royalty on three occasions. The mine's life was curtailed in depth at the opening of this century due to the depression in the price of tin and working finally ceased in 1914.

N.G.R. SW 362337.

The buildings centred around Marriott's shaft on the South Frances section of the Basset Mines are a conspicuous feature of the landscape to the south of Carn Brea. The engine house is a squat looking structure unlike the normal type of "Cornish castle". It housed an inverted compound engine with two cylinders of 40″ and 80″ using high pressure steam, built in Leeds by Hathorn Davy & Co. By using an inverted beam, the huge engine house was dispensed with and the walls were not required to bear any great weight. South Frances Mine was sunk on to the Great Flat Lode which, at this one mine alone produced over 66,500 tons of $8\frac{1}{2}\%$ copper ore. The Basset Mines closed down in 1919 owing to high pumping costs and impoverishment of the ore values in depth.

N.G.R. SW 680395.

Interior of the engine-house at Marriott's shaft. The large foundations which supported the beam and other parts of the engine can be seen in the foreground, whilst the circular brick-lined shaft is visible through the arch at the end. It was proposed to sink this shaft to a depth of 500 fathoms or more but this was never done and it remains 310 fathoms deep.

N.G.R. SW 680395.

The whim and pumping engine-houses at Fortescue's shaft, Wheal Grenville. The house which contained the pumping engine is particularly large (background) and contained a 90″ engine which, due to heavy water problems, was augmented by others on the sett. The huge circular shaft here is filled almost to the collar with water, 2370′ deep. *N.G.R. SW 668387.*

Two views of the preserved 90″ engine at Taylor's shaft, East Pool and Agar mine. One illustration shows the beam or bob, to the nose of which are suspended the wooden pump rods. The other picture shows the grille over the shaft collar, raising main from the pump and the balance bob. The engine worked for many years on Carn Brea Mines but was bought by E.P. & A. mine in 1924. She worked at the 1700′ deep Taylor's shaft until 1954 and is now preserved by the C.E.P.S.   *N.G.R. SW 677419.*

Cylinder cover, rod and valve gear of Robinson's 80″ engine at South Crofty. This engine is over a hundred years old and had the distinction of being the last Cornish engine to work on a Cornish mine. She made her last stroke on 1st May 1955, after electric pumps had been installed in the workings. Although in the care of the C.E.P.S., the engine is not accessible to the public due to still being on a working mine.
N.G.R. SW 662409.

Close by the A30 road at Pool stands Cornwall's last beam type whim engine. It is a 30″ built by Holman Bros in 1887. This wound from the shaft over which a large headframe was erected. It was capable of winding ore at the speed of 1000′ a minute with the engine working at 27 strokes a minute. Known as East Pool North Whim, it is in the care of the C.E.P.S. and is open for public inspection.

N.G.R. SW 676415.

Although these arsenic calciners have been removed at South Crofty, they are included because of their uniqueness. Arsenic was, at many tin mines an important by-product and found a ready market in America for the eradication of the cotton boll weevil. The arsenical pyrites found in conjunction with cassiterate was calcined in furnaces and the resultant condensate or soot was then scraped off the walls of long flues which led from the furnace. This soot, which was white, was then packed into barrels and exported.

N.G.R. SW 662409.

At Tolvaddon in the Tuckingmill valley stand two blackened arsenic stacks which served the condensing flues belonging to East Pool mine. The flues, which here were in excess of 42000 cubic feet capacity, were locally known as "lambreths". The height of the stacks serving arsenic furnaces was necessarily great as the smoke emitted contained poisonous fumes which were detrimental to the surrounding area. At Levant mine, where a similar arsenic plant was operating, the villagers who lived nearby frequently complained of the smoke poisoning both land and livestock.

N.G.R. SW 659417.

Examples of "old men's" workings can be seen on the cliffs near the old harbour at St. Agnes. Here a tin lode has been worked by early shafts which can be traced in the sides of the subsequent opened out workings. The shafts are to be seen in perfect cross section and are similar to those discovered at the Esperanza mine at Rio Tinto, Spain, although these, of course, are not so old. Traces of copper staining can be seen in places. The water leat seen running along the top of the workings, is a comparatively recent structure made in connection with dressing operations of Wheal Friendly nearby.

N.G.R. SW 719518.

In Trevellas Coombe stand perhaps Cornwall's last remaining water powered stamps outside a protected site. The valley was once a hive of activity and the dressing of ore was carried out along almost the entire stream right down to the sea. The wheel which powered the stamps has become ruinous and only the hub is left, which is made of cast iron. Of the twelve heads of stamps only six of the heads remain. However, sufficient still exists to give an idea how these machines, once a familiar feature in the landscape of the Duchy, were operated. *N.G.R. SW 729515.*

Discharging into Restronguet Creek near Bissoe is the county's greatest drainage system. Known as the Great County Adit, this long drainage tunnel, with branches to mines in the Gwennap, Chacewater and Scorrier district, is about 30 miles in length. When the mines were working and discharging water into the adit in 1839, the measured flow from the portal was 10,000 gallons a minute. There is still a considerable flow from this system which, during its heyday, was in places driven as two parallel tunnels due to the large quantity of water it was required to pass. Today, the portal, sited at the end of a cutting, is not easily seen, due to the amount of undergrowth and silting around its entrance.   *N.G.R. SW 763419.*

Of the many hundreds of drainage adits driven from the coast, Polberro adit is a typical one. Situated at the bottom of Trevaunance Coombe, St. Agnes, its water discharges on to the beach where hundreds of holidaymakers laze in the summer. Polberro mine is an old one with a record of working in 1600. It is an amalgamation of a number of small workings and enjoyed the reputation of being the richest tin mine in Cornwall during part of the nineteenth century. Following a visit by Queen Victoria in 1846, the mine was re-named Royal Polberro Consols.

N.G.R. SW 722517.

Wheal Coates is well known if only because of its spectacular position on the cliff edge between St. Agnes Head and Chapel Porth. From the sands below, at low water, the lode can be seen in the face of the cliff, together with the large adit cave in which ore has been stoped leaving openings at the top. The drainage adit is at the back of the cave and the water from it cascades down in a small waterfall; the interior of the cave is an awe-inspiring place. The engine house is that on the Towanroath shaft which is 104 fathoms deep. This was never a particularly rich venture and was worked intermittently until 1889. It was re-opened in 1911 but finally closed in 1913. A plan to open the mine once again in 1929 never reached fruition and the site has been silent now for over half a century.   *N.G.R. SW 699502.*

A general view of the Wheal Kitty dressing floors with the engine houses of Wheal Friendly and **Polberro** on the skyline. The ground around Wheal Kitty is a mass of burrows, shafts and leats and should be inspected with care.   *N.G.R. SW 725515.*

Extensive dressing floors such as those at Wheal Kitty near St. Agnes were found at most large mines. However, as the mine was re-worked in the early nineteen hundreds, and as much use was made of concrete at that time, this floor is perhaps better preserved than most. Circular buddles and accompanying leats are a conspicuous feature of the site.   *N.G.R. SW 725515.*

The pumping engine-house of Wheal Coates, showing the shaft collar and foundations of the balance bob to the right. The house contained a 60″ engine but this was not used when the mine was re-worked early this century, a small horizontal engine being used for this period. Behind the house are to be seen the foundations of the boiler house, placed there due to the site being on the cliff edge.

N.G.R. SW 699502.

Higher up the cliff stand the remains of the whim and stamps engine houses. The whole site is now in the care of the National Trust and unlike many fine cliff-top mine buildings which have been demolished, these engine houses will be afforded the protection they deserve. They stand as a tribute to the skill of some long dead masons who laboured to build them.

N.G.R. SW 699502.

This massive engine-house, sited at the northern end of the East Wheal Rose sett, contained a famous 100″ pumping engine built by Harveys of Hayle. The house and the engine which laboured inside it, were the largest that Cornwall has ever seen. However, the engine which was used to drain the mine during the time it was re-worked in 1884, was only used for about twelve months, the venture being wound up a year later. An engine of such mammoth proportions was required due to the mine being heavily watered. Prior to this re-working, the mine had been flooded by a cloudburst in 1847 causing the death of 40 miners working underground. Since that date the mine is said to have never been completely unwatered.

N.G.R. SW 839558.

Close by the A390 road east of Scorrier, the graceful stack of Killifreth mine has become a well-known landmark. Apart from very early stacks, all engine-house chimneys were built of brick near the top, due to brick being an easier material to use on the narrowest and thinly walled crown. Coupled with this, less scaffolding was needed for these lighter bricks than for granite. The higher the stack, the greater the draught in the fires of the steam raising boilers of the engines and when a larger engine was erected at Killifreth in 1914, the brick crown of the stack was doubled in height.　*N.G.R. SW 733443.*

A fine example of a Cornish engine shaft can also be seen at Killifreth. Of typical rectangular section, the shaft has a concrete collar with the foundations of the balance bob beside it. Known as Hawke's or Richard's shaft it is 136 fathoms deep, the walls being lined with timber.

N.G.R. SW 733443.

Great Wheal Busy has various claims to fame, not the least being that it was here that that celebrated engineer John Smeaton erected his first modified Newcomen engine. It was here also that the first Watt separate condensing pumping engine was subsequently erected. It is also one of the oldest copper mines in the county. The last engine to occupy the house shown here was an 85″ second-hand engine which remained until 1946 when it was finally broken up.

Opposite the engine-house at Great Wheal Busy are the other buildings associated with a large mine such as the smiths' shop and materials store. Although the windows of these buildings have been covered with corrugated iron, the lintels over the doorways are visible and are of great interest. Each one is in the form of a large cast-iron beam bearing the words—WILLIAMS PERRAN FOUNDRY. GREAT WHEAL (1872) BUSY MINES. The date is significant as it was in that year that the mine was to witness a disastrous re-working, costing a vast amount of money, which ended in failure less than twelve months later. *N.G.R. SW 744448.*

Wheal Ellen, south east of Porthtowan, is unusual in that the top of the stack is castellated, a feature shared by only a few mines in the county. Frequently such ornate additions to houses and stacks were incorporated in the drawings of the engineer responsible for construction but were often omitted when building took place. Not far away, at Gooninis Mine, St. Agnes, a similarly embellished stack can be seen.

N.G.R. SW 703468.

Usually engine-houses were built of granite, as this material has great strength which is a prerequisite for such load bearing structures. However, standing beside Cook's shaft at South Crofty is a large engine-house built entirely of concrete. This was built in 1922 to house a 90″ pumping engine purchased from the defunct Basset Mines which was needed quickly due to the threat of flooding in South Crofty by the closure of East Pool nearby. Over 7000 tons of concrete was required to complete the house. In just six months from digging the foundations the building was ready to receive the engine. *N.G.R. SW 664412.*

It was a costly business to transport heavy engine parts from the Midlands where they were first made, to the mines in Cornwall. It was not long therefore, that foundries capable of such work sprang up within the area. One such foundry was Harvey's at Hayle who were responsible for the building and erection of many great engines throughout the world.

After nearly a century of successful business, the foundry closed down in 1895 but the site still retains some of the old structures as well as the pond which supplied water to the wheels used to provide power to the works. Some of the huge casting and machine shop buildings are to be seen alongside the B3302 road to Helston.   *N.G.R. SW 558372.*

The great copper mines in the St. Day and Gwennap area were supplied with pumping engines and other machinery by the Perran Foundry, situated on a small inlet of the River Fal near Perranarworthal. Started in 1791, the foundry expanded in conjunction with the demand created by the adjacent mining district and subsequently became as famous as Harvey's. The site is now owned by a firm of millers but from the gateway, two cast iron arches are visible bearing the name of the foundry over the old entrance to the works at the opposite side of the yard.   *N.G.R. SW 775382.*

High on the hill north-west of Calstock stands the engine-house, boiler-house and stack of Wheal Edward. This was never a very rich mine and has witnessed several separate workings, the last being in 1918. In an area renowned for the production of numerous minerals, Wheal Edward is known to have produced copper as the major mineral and also small quantities of pyrite, wolfram and arsenic. *N.G.R. SX 427701.*

At the south-east edge of Bodmin Moor is a heavily mineralised tract of copper ground centred on Caradon Hill. Huge burrows and gaunt engine-house ruins adorn the hillside here, the most impressive perhaps being those of South Caradon. This deep and rich mine was opened in 1837 and between that date and 1885 produced 217,820 tons of copper. The engine shaft here has been used as a rubbish tip; oil drums and old cars fill it to the collar.

N.G.R. SX 269698.

Morwellham Quay, at the terminus of the tramways from Devon Great Consols and the Tavistock canal. This quay, paved with small tiles or bricks, was once busy with piles of copper ore awaiting shipment down the River Tamar. The berths where the vessels lay whilst loading are now choked with weeds, although it is hoped that much of the overgrown remains of these will be cleared in conjunction with restoration work now in progress.

N.G.R. SX 445695.

The deep Tamar valley was ideal for drainage purposes and also presented a steep flank from which exploratory adits could be driven. One such adit is found some 700 yards south of Gunnislake Bridge. Known as North Impham mine, it was an insignificant venture about which little is recorded. Red ochrous water issues from the portal.

N.G.R. SX 434719.

The engine-house of Wheal Betsy, one of Dartmoor's most famous mines, stands close beside the A386 road north of Mary Tavy. Affixed to the north wall of the house is a metal plaque which reads "This ancient silver-lead mine was reopened in 1806 and worked successfully for the next seventy years. The mine was worked by water power until 1868 when this building was erected to house a Cornish beam pumping engine. Until its closure in 1877 all pumping, winding and crushing of ore was carried out by steam power. In 1967 the ruined engine house and stack were acquired and made safe by the National Trust as a memorial to the mining industry of Dartmoor."

N.G.R. SX 510814.

The Mendips

To the student of mining history the ancient Mendip region is rather lacking in remains and is therefore somewhat disappointing. Whilst lead and calamine (zinc) have been worked vigorously from Roman times until the opening years of this century, all this activity was undertaken by small groups of "old men" whose workings today are largely filled in or have subsequently collapsed. This has resulted in large tracts of disturbed ground comprising old shaft hollows and small hillocks, known in the area as Warrens. As the ore was found at relatively shallow horizons, these old workings seldom reached depth greater than 20 to 30 fathoms.

The limestone of the district is riddled with water swallows into which surface water sinks and this has resulted in famous natural cave systems such as those connected with the River Axe. Often the lead miner broke into these caves during his search for mineral, a classic case being that of the discovery and working in the Lamb Leer Cavern. As water on the Mendips was scarce, the miners took their ore to regional dressing floors called mineries where the ore was dressed and smelted.

The Mendips is similar in many ways to the Peak District and had a code of mining laws with special courts to enforce them. For this purpose, the mining field was divided into four Liberties, each with its own court and minery. The four mineries concerned can be traced today, with the ruined walls of the old smelt mills accompanied by overgrown water leats and dams. They are to be found at or near Charterhouse, Smitham's Hill, Priddy and Chewton.

As has been said, little is to be seen today in comparison with a similar field such as the Peak District and open shafts are few in number. However, one such shaft can be seen north of the road crossing Velvet Bottom, Charterhouse. With its attendant rusty winch, it is obvious that the site is a recent one where an old shaft **(seen below) has been re-opened and subsequently abandoned.**

N.G.R. ST 505556.

Wales

The chief minerals worked in Wales were copper, lead, zinc and gold. The gold of Wales was known to the Romans and there is conclusive proof that it was actually mined by them at Dolaucothi in Carmarthenshire.

The Dolaucothi gold mines are situated on land now owned by the National Trust and access, therefore, presents no problems. In places the hillside is riddled with cave-like openings (or ogofau) whilst the largest site is a great open-work, resembling a quarry, now utilised as a caravan park. Before entering the openwork, a small monolith exhibiting deep tooling marks can be seen, thought to be either a crushing stone or, more likely, a form of whetstone. Deep drainage levels (gated) are seen near the floor of the open work, whilst stopes are present in the sides. The tank or reservoir which was fed by the leat is to be found near the road to Caeo above the quarry. In recent times a company sank an 80 fathom shaft on the site but the venture was a failure and remains of this last working consist merely of a few concrete foundations and a concrete cap to the shaft.

Further north in Merionethshire, the Dolgellau gold belt has many interesting remains. Centred around the tributaries of the Afon Mawddach, these gold deposits have attracted the attention of many adventurers since the middle of the last century and in fact, are still doing so. Probably the most interesting of the mines is Gwynfynydd with its attendant concentrating mill to the south. This mine, from which the regal metal was extracted, is also situated in surroundings of equal beauty. It cannot be reached by car but the walk up the side of the river (passing the levels of Tyddyn Gwladys gold mine) is superb. The mill is the first to be reached, lying at the confluence of the Afon Mawddach and Afon Gain. The site is now tranquil but must formerly have been a hive of activity containing as it did, stone breakers and a battery of stamps of 40 heads, all of which were powered by a water turbine. Gwyfynydd Mine lies about half a mile further upstream and is reached by walking along what was once the tramway connecting mine and mill. Other small gold mines such as Vigra, St. David's, Garthgell, Cambrian, Voel Ispri and Wnion occupy positions in the mountains, a mile or so north of Mawddach Estuary.

Copper was mined at various locations around Snowdon and Dolgellau in Caernarvonshire and Merionethshire respectively, but the most important of mines producing the red metal was the Parys copper mine on Anglesey. Although worked from ancient times, the mine was 're-discovered' in 1768 and subsequently became the richest copper producer in Europe, seriously competing with the Cornish copper industry with its attendant deeper mining problems. After its opening, Parys Mine was worked by adits and shafts but extensive stoping later produced a major collapse of the workings, resulting in subsequent mining by open cast method. During the eighteenth century, over 40,000 tons of metal was won from the mountain. Working finished in 1883 due to exhaustion of payable ore reserves. Since then, copper has been recovered on a small scale from mine drainage water by a precipitation process using scrap iron. Further east, copper was worked at the Llandudno copper mine situated at the foot of Great Ormes Head. Little now remains of this venture which was abandoned about a century ago because of flooding by sea water through hidden fissures.

Cardiganshire has been the most important county in mid-Wales for the production of galena, followed closely by Montgomeryshire. Broadly speaking, this mining field is bounded by the Dovey valley in the north, Caersws in the east, Tregaron in the south, and westwards by the coast; the great concentration of mines occurring close to the valleys of the rivers Ystwyth and Rheidol.

Due to the mountainous nature of the land, coal was difficult to obtain and therefore steam power was seldom utilised. Considerable use was made of water power and many miles of leats can be found which often served various mines en route. Occasionally a waterwheel was situated some distance from the mine, the power of the wheel being transmitted by reciprocating flat rods over the ground to the pumping shaft. At Bwadrain Mine, three quarters of a mile south of Cwmbrwyno, near Devil's Bridge, a line of such flat rods extended half a mile from a waterwheel erected in the Rheidol valley, by way of a 700 foot slope to the pumping shaft situated in a peat flat above the valley.

Of great interest and easily accessible by road from Devil's Bridge, is Cwmystwyth Mine. One cannot fail to be impressed by the amount of activity which has left its mark here. The whole hillside is a mass of spoil heaps, ruined buildings, levels and shafts. A large tenement building stands by the roadside bearing a strong resemblance to the 'lodging shop' of the Northern Pennine mines. The mine was, in fact, owned by a Yorkshireman at the beginning of the nineteenth century. The mill itself remains in quite good condition, whilst the main level of the mine can still be seen.

Near Ponterwyd, an extensive water leat can be traced which served the Llywernog, Powel United and Clara Consols mines. Various rivers were tapped by this leat, the main source of water being the Gladwr stream. The leat is six or seven miles in length and has a loss in level of only 50 feet, a remarkable feat in engineering.

Other notable mines in Cardiganshire include Fron-goch, near Pontrhydygroes, which still has a crumbling engine-house on the site; Bronfloyd, Tirymynach which is said to be one of the oldest mines of the county, and Bryndyfi near the village of Furnace on the Dovey estuary. The last named has many water wheel pits and remains of the ancillary buildings.

Near Llanidloes are to be found the remains of the richest lead mine in Montgomeryshire which included its own railway built in 1872 to transport ore to the main line at Caersws. This was the Van Mine, which in 1870, five years after its discovery, employed 500 men and eventually reached a depth of 150 fathoms below adit. Ore from the haulage shaft on the slopes of the hill above was carried down by an incline tramway and through a tunnel to the lower dressing floors, three in number and spaced at intervals up the hill slope. Power on the middle and top two floors was provided by steam engines and two stacks for these remain today on the highest floor. Water power was utilised for the lower dressing plant. The mine closed down in 1892, after producing over 96,000 tons of lead concentrates. Exploration of the site today can be an absorbing undertaking; some of the buildings which housed machinery on the middle dressing floor, being still used by a local resident for other purposes.

Wherever one travels in the mountains of Wales, remnants of metalliferous mining are in evidence. A small isolated spoil heap will often reveal an adit portal above, evidence of a long abandoned trial for mineral. Even the celebrated Pistyll Rhaeadr waterfall near Llanchaeadr-Ym-Mochnant, in Denbighshire, visited by George Borrow on his tour of Wales in 1854, provided a source of water for a leat still to be seen cut in the rock face and which supplied the nearby Craig-y-Mwn Lead Mine.

The hillside at the Dolaucothi Roman gold mines is riddled with caves, some of which are quite deep. These are found above the large opencast working and are probably the earliest workings on the site. Some "caves" —large adits driven into the hillside—can be recognised as trial levels and end after a short distance at a blank face.
N.G.R. SN 666404.

A view inside one of the Dolaucothi caves. Sunlight streams through the entrance which is located high up on the side of the opencast.
N.G.R. SN 664403.

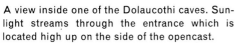

The levels driven in Dolaucothi are often in the form of an inverted horse shoe. It has been suggested that they were driven in this fashion to facilitate the passage of miners on whose shoulders were carried yokes on which were suspended bags of veinstuff and other materials.

At the bottom of the opencast, two drainage adits can be seen. The portals are of small dimensions and have been gated for safety reasons.
N.G.R. SN 663403.

Perhaps the most remarkable feature of the Roman gold mines is the water leat. This artificial watercourse was seven miles long and ran from the River Cothi near Bwlch-y-rhiw to deliver water to the reservoir above the opencast. It ran between the 600′ and 800′ contours on the eastern side of the valley. At various places throughout its course it was carried over difficult terrain in launders and in cuttings. It is easily seen on the hillside above the opencast at a point where it starts the descent to the reservoir. The water was required for dressing operations and for driving crude crushing mills.

N.G.R. SN 665403.

On the north bank of the River Ystwyth near Devil's Bridge lie the extensive remains of Cwmystwyth lead mine. This continued in production until 1916 and much of the concentrating mill remains. The ore hoppers at the rear of the building received the mineral from the mine which, in stages, was crushed, washed, jigged and concentrated as it proceeded "downhill" through the mill. In the foreground are the concrete foundations of the compressor house which also supplied extra power to the mill when required. The compressor plant was driven by a 168 horse-power Pelton wheel using a 741′ head of water supplied through pipes down the hillside from a lake above.

N.G.R. SN 803746.

General view of the Cwmystwyth mine looking north-east. In the foreground is the mine office, behind which is the mill. The whole of the northern hillside is scarred with mining activity whilst on the opposite side of the river spoil heaps and excavations denote the site of the smaller South Cwmystwyth mine. *N.G.R. SN 803746.*

Of the many levels driven to the veins at Cwmystwyth, Bonsall's Level or Level Fawr is the most important. The roughly built portal once contained a plaque which read: CWMYSTWYTH MINING CO. LTD. RE-OPENED 1898, HY. GEMMAN, MANAGING DIRECTOR. Unfortunately this has recently vanished. Other levels driven on the mine include Rosa Level (the highest), Mitchell's Level, Kingside adit whilst near the road are the remains of the collapsed Pugh's Adit and Gill's Lower Level. *N.G.R. SN 806748.*

A view of the mine buildings at Llywernog lead mine, near Ponterwyd. The chief buildings still remaining are an office, mill ruins, water-wheel pit and a powder magazine. The office is distinctive in having decorated window and door surrounds executed in yellow brickwork.

N.G.R. SN 733809.

At Llywernog, water power was extensively used, provided by a long and well engineered leat over six miles in length. Power for pumping and crushing the ore was supplied by a water wheel 50′ in diameter which was erected about 1875. The pit in which this wheel operated remains, together with the axle bearings at each side. The engine shaft at the mine is now filled in but reached a depth of 72 fathoms.   *N.G.R. SN 733809.*

The powder house at the mine is only a small building. As is usual, it has no windows and is set some distance away from the rest of the site.   *N.G.R. SN 732810.*

The entrance to Number 5 level, Gwynfynydd gold mine. This is the largest and most important level in the area and was the scene of a rich strike of gold bearing ore in 1895. After a drive of about 550′, the level emerges into a large cavern in which stands a wooden headframe over the flooded collar of an incline shaft. The buildings on the right include a strong room, office and workshops.

N.G.R. SN 737282.

The strong-room door to the room where all visible gold was placed prior to transportation to the mill. This door was bought from Dolgellau gaol in 1878. *N.G.R. SN 737282.*

The headframe at the head of the incline shaft in Number 5 level. The incline which was 300′ long and 160′ deep was provided with two sets of rails on which ore trams operated. The laden tram was wound up the incline (whilst the other empty one was returned to the bottom), and, on reaching the top of the headframe, discharged its load into a hopper incorporated within the structure. These hoppers were in turn discharged into trams which transported the ore out of the level and down to the mill.

The earliest workings for gold on Clogau can be seen high up near the top of the mountain. They take the form of deep open stopes which are usually associated with trial and working levels in the vicinity. Often these levels are flooded. The photograph shows such an open stope, more reminiscent of Derbyshire than the Welsh mountains.

N.G.R. SH 675201.

The St. David's Gold Mine continues to attract speculators on whom the lure of gold has a pronounced effect. The main working entrance to the mine is the Llechfraith level shown in the photograph. At the time this was taken (1971) reworking the mine was in progress which accounts for the compressor and other dressing machinery at the level mouth. Between 1900 and 1905, 43,155 ounces of gold were produced from the Clogau area.

N.G.R. SH 668194.

The mill, half a mile downstream, was driven by a water turbine. This was supplied with water through a cast iron pipe which still remains. The penstock above this is also in good condition. The turbine was installed as late as the 1930's, steam having been used before this date. Operations at both mine and mill came to an end in 1938.

N.G.R. SN 736275.

The Parys Copper Mines are unique in a number of ways not the least being in the arrangement of the pumping gear. On the summit is the remains of a windmill used to assist a nearby steam pumping engine and connected to it by flat rods. This arrangement greatly reduced coal consumption. To the east, the ivy clad remains of an engine house mark the site of Pearl Shaft. The engine here was coupled to a separate outside bob working directly over the shaft collar. This engine additionally pumped water up the hillside to a supply reservoir for a further engine sited some 150′ above. *N.G.R. SH 447907.*

Halkyn mountain north of Mold, has been worked for lead from Roman times. Subsequently, during the eighteenth and nineteenth centuries these mines were deepened and in so doing ran into such water difficulties that they could be justifiably classed as the wettest mines in Europe. Two deep levels, the Halkyn and Milwr, were constructed to drain the area in 1818 and 1896 respectively. The Milwr tunnel is at sea level and has its outfall at Bagillt. It is over ten miles long from its portal to the final intersection with the Cathole vein near Mold. This never failing water supply is utilised by an adjacent factory. *N.G.R. SJ 222754.*

Shropshire

The mines of Shropshire are centred around the villages of Shelve, Habberley and Ritton Castle. The chief mineral worked was lead, with small amounts of zinc and barytes being raised earlier this century. Roman remains have been found in the Shelve district at Roman Gravels Mine. Here the ore was easily worked where it cropped out of the hillsides. The remains found included wooden shovels, candles with hempen wicks, pottery and coins. In addition to these, three Roman pigs of lead (or ingots) have come to light, one of which is to be seen in the British Museum, the other in Liverpool Museum.

Subsequent mining in the eighteenth and nineteenth centuries was undertaken through shafts, some of which were extremely deep. The engine shaft on Snailbeach Mine, for instance, was sunk to a depth of 231 fathoms.

Deep mining required the use of steam pumping engines, a number of houses for these remaining today. In addition, many mines had a drainage adit. These were occasionally a co-operative venture draining more than one mine, as is the case with the Boat Level. This level, about $2\frac{3}{4}$ miles long, served the Bog, Pennerly, Tankerville and Burgam Mines and was adapted—as the name suggests—as an underground canal for the transportation of ore. The boats were propelled by miners who pulled themselves along by grasping a rope that ran along the level wall. The portal of the Boat Level has collapsed but water still escapes through the fall a few hundred yards north of Burgam Mine at Shelve.

Another major drainage system which was started but never reached its objective was the Leigh Level, driven from Leigh Hall near Minsterly with the object of draining the East Roman Gravels workings two miles away. Started in 1825, it was sporadically driven until 1923 when it was finally abandoned. The portal is still open. Finally, the third drainage level of any importance was known as the Wood Level. The portal of this adit, by the stream in Hope Valley, has been built up to form a weir and a considerable amount of water still flows from it. This level drained the Grits, Ladywell, Roman Gravels and East Roman Gravels mines.

The largest of the mines in the region is Snailbeach, the extensive dumps and buildings of which can be seen from afar. It has the reputation of having produced the largest volume of lead for area worked in the world. A minor railway was constructed to it, the course of which can be traced to the point where it joined the Minsterly line at Pontesbury.

An ore bogie at Snailbeach in 1968, a rare relic of the 1914-18 era when the mine was worked for barytes.   *N.G.R. SJ 376022.*

The smoke from the boilers of the Snailbeach pumping engine was conveyed to the stack by a long flue. The stack was some distance away and higher up the hill whereby a greater draught was created in the furnace. The flue, similar in construction to those in the mid-Pennine smelting mills, is made of arched masonry covered with earth and is seen here near the base of the stack.   *N.G.R. SJ 374020.*

Engine house at the pumping shaft on Snailbeach mine. The ladder shaft nearby was the scene of a disaster in 1895 when the wire rope of the cage broke in the shaft (252 yds deep) sending seven men to their death below.   *N.G.R. SJ 374022.*

Inside the Snailbeach engine-house, a scene taken from the bottom of the cataract pit looking towards the rear of the house. The bolts that secured the cylinder of the 61″ Cornish engine are still visible in the floor.   *N.G.R. SJ 374022.*

A ruinous headframe marks the site of Black Tom Shaft on part of the extensive Snailbeach Sett. Although a mere 20 fathoms deep and not the main shaft on the mine, it was nevertheless the last to be used when the Black Tom vein was producing barytes during the First World War. About 5000 tons of this material was mined per year during that time. Barytes was milled at Cliffdale Mill in the nearby Hope Valley, where the mine's drainage adit discharges into a tributary of the Rea Brook.

N.G.R. SJ 374023.

At Crowsnest, two miles south of Minsterly, is to be seen the small engine-house and stack of New Central Mine, sometimes known as New Central Snailbeach or South Salop. The mine worked five veins but never achieved anything like the same output as its more northerly neighbour, Snailbeach. The engine shaft is open but flooded, as the adit driven from Hope Valley to drain the mine has collapsed.   *N.G.R. SJ 369016.*

Alderley Edge

Alderley Edge, in Cheshire, has been known for its copper deposits from early times and stone axes and hammers that are believed to belong to the Bronze Age have been found in ancient workings here. The three most important mines are the Engine Vein Mine, the Wood Mine and the West Mine, the two latter being set back some distance from the Edge itself. The ore was found mainly in sandstone and could easily be worked by pick and shovel but even so, little timbering was used underground as the roof was sufficiently strong to be left unsupported.

Opencast workings and cave-like hollows abound on the Edge and in the Wood Mine extensive stoping has been carried out. The records show the output of copper ore from the area totalled 168,269 tons, between the years 1857 and 1877.

Old Engine Rake bears a marked resemblance to a typical Derbyshire rake. The stoping of the copper here has resulted in quite large caverns along this vein which can be explored easily, although with caution. This working is perhaps the best example of mining on the Edge because all the buildings and levels of the West and Wood mines have now been destroyed. Being close to the great conurbation of Manchester, the Alderley mines have been the scene of several tragedies where youngsters, ill-equipped and without the necessary experience, explored the mines, often with fatal consequences. All of the entrances to the more extensive workings have now been sealed as a result.

N.G.R. SJ 861776.

An early working on the back of a vein.   *N.G.R. SJ 861778.*

A mined 'cave' adit on the Edge, of early date.   *N.G.R. SJ 862780.*

Ecton Copper Mines

Ecton Hill lies about two miles west of the Derbyshire county boundary, in Staffordshire. This smooth elliptical limestone hill, some 1200' in height, was abundantly rich in copper which was worked at three principal mines. These were the Goodhope-Dutchman-Bag group, Deep Ecton and Clayton. The first named complex was the earliest working and it was here that gunpowder was first used in Britain about 1670. Deep Ecton was opened up by an adit at river level (where the Manifold runs around the west of the hill), whilst a shaft sunk from the hilltop was used for winding ore from below adit level. A Boulton and Watt engine wound from this shaft, which attained the depth of 220 fathoms from the collar. The remains of the engine-house here can still be seen. Ore was found *en masse* in great bell-shaped deposits, the stopes which can be entered today above adit level. There a large underground engine chamber exists which housed a water-wheel used for pumping, the water being conveyed to this through an aqueduct tunnel driven into the hillside.

Also scattered over the hill are various smaller mines such as Waterbank and East Ecton, plus others which were little more than trials. It is said that the Duke of Devonshire who owned the mineral rights at Ecton, was able to pay for the building of the famous Crescent at Buxton out of earnings made from these mines.

The chief danger in exploration of these interesting old mines is the deep flooded winzes that fill the passages in places. The Clayton and Dutchman mines are particularly subject to this. This winze fills the main level in the Dutchman mine and has been bridged with planks of doubtful age and strength.

◀

The western face of the hill, showing Deep Ecton adit portal near the river, Clayton adit portal beside the road, the spoil heap of Dutchman Level and on the summit, the old engine-house of Deep Ecton drawing shaft. *N.G.R. SK 097581.*

◀

Deep Ecton adit portal. This was the main drainage and access level of this famous old mine and connects with the engine chamber at the bottom of the drawing shaft. The shaft actually went down much deeper but now is flooded to adit level. The engine-house which contained the Boulton and Watt winding engine can be seen as a mound on the skyline. The engine wound ore to the Salt's Level which emerges half way up the hillside. This was connected to the dressing floors which were also on the same contour. Deep Ecton adit has collapsed just inside the portal and the keystone to the arch bearing the letters "R.S. 1774" is now missing.

N.G.R. SK 097582.

The extraction of ore in the Ecton mines has left huge caverns, some of which are partially packed with "deads" or waste rock. The illustration shows part of such a stope in the Goodhope-Dutchman-Bag complex.

The Peak District

The Carboniferous limestone hills of Derbyshire have been intensively worked for lead from ancient times but, with a very few exceptions, only by comparatively small groups of adventurers with little capital.

The outcome of all this activity over the centuries is not at first easily recognisable. Because of the abundance of steep valleys, drainage levels called soughs were utilised and thus the need for steam pumping engines was not as great as in those areas such as Cornwall, without such valleys. Remains of engine-houses do exist but only on mines which had sufficient capital to install them and where deep payable ore values warranted the expense.

It is therefore, the smaller sites in Derbyshire which make up the majority of interesting remains. Each small mine had a shaft from which the ore was hauled by means of a jack roller or stowe (hand windlass) and often, in addition, a separate climbing shaft, through which the miners gained access to the workings. Occasionally, these climbing shafts, which were never more than about 2' 6" diameter, can be seen with footholes cut into the side or projecting stones on which the miners placed their feet.

The buildings associated with these small ventures were very rudimentary, consisting usually of a coe built over the climbing shaft in which the miner kept his tools, and a bing stead or ore store. Sometimes this latter was dispensed with, the ore being stored in the coe itself. Remains of these coes, built of rough unmortared lime stone, can be found, particularly on Bonsall Moor, Matlock, and Bradwell Moor, Castleton.

Buddles, in which the ore was separated from the waste rock after being roughly crushed with a bucking hammer, are often found in close proximity to a mine. These are sloping, stone-lined channels down which water was run, the ore being raked across the head of the buddle, thus allowing the water to separate the lighter rock from the heavier ore. Sometimes, crushing was done by means of heavy circular stones turned by horses around a paved or iron track. Crushing circles are quite a common feature in the Castleton area, although numbers of these have recently been destroyed by fluorspar recovery operations on the old dumps near the mines.

Many open rakes, sometimes of great length and depth, are a common feature of Derbyshire. Dirtlow Rake at Castleton, is an example of such an excavation, as also are the Roman and Fern caves in High Tor grounds, Matlock. Also in Matlock Bath, on the opposite side of the dale, the hillside is honeycombed with mine workings, of which the Rutland Cavern (now a show cave) is reputedly of Roman origin. Others, like the Royal, Wapping, Cumberland and Devonshire Mines, have been extensively worked for fluorspar in more recent times.

The Speedwell Mine at Castleton is well known as a tourist attraction where boating trips along a flooded level end at the "Bottomless Pit". This level was driven to intersect the Faucet Rake in depth, which was found to have been washed out, leaving a large natural cavern.

Remains of larger undertakings which warranted steam engines for drainage can be found at Old End Mine, Crich; Mandale Mine, Lathkilldale; Old Mill Close Mine, Darley Dale; New Engines Mine, Eyam Edge; and Magpie Mine, Sheldon. The last named engine-house and buildings is perhaps the best preserved site, being the field centre of the Peak District Mines Historical Society. This Society is renovating the site of Good Luck Mine at Via Gellia, a fairly typical example of a medium-sized Derbyshire lead mine.

Of an estimated total of over 200 soughs which have been driven for drainage purposes, many of the outfalls or "tails" of these levels can be seen today. These are usually found in valley bottoms, permitting maximum depth of drainage and allowing the escaping water to find a ready outlet in a nearby stream or river. The earliest large-scale sough in Derbyshire was probably the Cromford Sough near Matlock which was driven to the Gang vein in 1673 by Cornelius Vermuyden. Water still issues from the tail of this level in wet weather.

Soughs were also used as pumpways at mines which made use of steam and hydraulic engines when sunk to a lower horizon than the sough. Hillcarr Sough in Darley Dale was a major drainage level of this nature, serving the rich mines in the Alport area. Important soughs of the eighteenth and nineteenth centuries include Yatestoop, Meerbrook, Oxclose, Mandale, Magpie and Calver, all of which are still open at the tail and flowing.

Finally, at most average sized lead mines, evidence can be found of horse gins, which were used for winding ore up deep shafts. These gins (or horse-engines) consisted of a vertical axle and drum with an upper bearing supported by massive cross members. This was placed adjacent to the shaft, over which a small headframe was mounted. The central axle drum holding the winding rope was turned by a horse which, harnessed to the axle, trod a circular path around it. The rope from the drum passed over pulleys in the headframe and winding was arranged on the counter balance principle, one rope being wound in whilst the other let out. The horse-path or gin-race usually had a low wall around it to give some weather protection to the horse. These are the circles or races and the accompanying walls which can be seen today, often with a pierced stone in the centre representing the footstep bearing of the drum axle. Horse gins were in general use throughout Britain and elsewhere until approximately the close of the last century.

Frequently, veins in Derbyshire can be picked out by a line of old men's workings which range across the fields. Such workings consist of shaft hollows and hillocks which, in the passage of years, have been grassed over. This old line of workings can be seen near the top of Deep Dale, near Sheldon.   *N.G.R. SK 160693.*

When a vein was sufficiently near the surface it was usually worked by opencast methods by the old man (or in the vernacular—"T'owd man"). These surface scratchings are often, but by no means always, a sign of early mining activity and are shown here on Bonsall Moor near Matlock.

N.G.R. SK 253594.

Climbing shafts are small and usually only 50′ or 60′ deep. They often go down in stages with a short intermediate level between each pitch. These two illustrations show a typical climbing shaft in the Whitelow Mines on Bonsall Moor. It is lined for most of the depth with rough unmortared limestone known as ginging. This was done until the shaft reached solid bedrock. For safety, shafts are invariably covered with stone built "beehives" although rotten planks and old bedsteads are not uncommon!

N.G.R. SK 253582.

These two illustrations show a typical drawing or engine shaft of a medium sized mine. Horse whims were used for drawing from such shafts, in this case the main shaft on Hard Rake Mine near Sheldon. This shaft is 330′ in depth and the water which can be seen at the bottom occupies 70′ of this.   *N.G.R. SK 163681.*

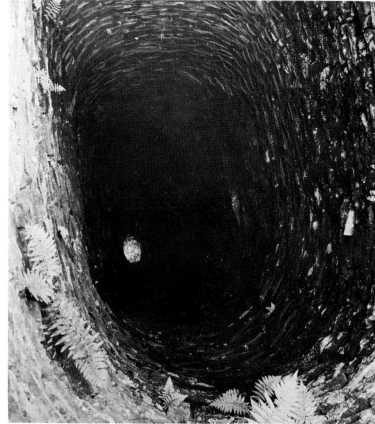

Climbing shafts are found in the middle of coes which were small mine buildings erected over them in which the miner kept his tools. These coes are now found in very derelict condition and over the years have been robbed of their stone for the repairing of field walls and barns. This coe is on a shaft on the Magpie vein west of Sheldon.

N.G.R. SK 165686.

The windlass or stowe played an important part in Derbyshire mining for not only did it provide a method of drawing from shallow shafts, but it was also a symbol of ownership to a mine. Until quite recently a stowe was to be seen over the shaft of the Lower Chance Mine at Hopton, perhaps the last of its kind to remain on a disused lead mine in the whole region.

N.G.R. SK 253548.

After being drawn to grass, the ore was crushed and treated in buddles which are occasionally discovered when walking the old mining areas. This typical buddle has recently been excavated on Bonsall Moor, lined with flat limestone blocks and built into the side of a mine hillock. Water for working the buddle would probably be drawn from an adjoining mine shaft, which has now run in.

N.G.R. SK 268570.

In Derbyshire the predominant type of vein is a near vertical ribbon of ore between limestone cheeks and is called a "rake". A rake can run for many miles across country, varying greatly in thickness. The galena is invariably accompanied by other minerals such as calcite, barytes and fluorspar which is collectively known as gangue. Taken underground at Putwell Hill Mine in Monsal Dale, this illustration shows a typical rake after the extraction of much of the vein.

N.G.R. SK 178718.

Some remarkable feats of mining are found in Derbyshire and give some idea of the perseverance of the old man at work. In Ball Eye Mine near Matlock, a sough is driven for hundreds of feet through solid limestone and executed in coffin level profile. Coffin Level, as the name implies, is a tunnel tapered at the roof and sole so as to just admit the human form. In this way the minimum of work was necessary in driving through hard rock.

This sough, known as Founterabbey in this section, was certainly driven before 1724 and it is thought that lime blasting was used in its construction. The sweeping pick marks on the walls and tooling marks in the roof are a feature of such levels. The water flowing along the sough is slightly thermal, as are many springs in the Matlock area.

The outfalls of Derbyshire soughs vary and can take the form of iron pipes, magnificently masoned arches, horse troughs or —as is the case with Tearsall Sough at Wensley—a form of ground level well. The sough drained the mines of the same name and it is thought that it was driven in the middle of the eighteenth century.　　　　　　　　*N.G.R. SK 262609.*

Stoke Sough, which drained part of the important Eyam Edge mines, has its outfall in the grounds of Stoke Hall near Grindleford. As the water which issues from this level is slightly thermal, a bath house has been built beside the portal by a former proprietor of the Hall. The bath house has steps leading down into the water which can be shut off so as to run out of the portal in the normal way. The water is conducted from this over an artificial waterfall to enhance the adjacent garden. The garden is now overgrown and forgotten as is also the bath house.　　　　　　　　*N.G.R. SK 241763.*

Said to be one of the oldest mines in Derbyshire, the Mandale Mine in Lathkilldale was being worked at least by the thirteenth century. The engine-house, built about 1874, is now in a ruinous state, with only the bob or lever wall standing. The steam engine was used to supplement an already over-worked water-wheel of about 35' diameter which occupied a pit to the right of the ruin. The mine closed in 1851 having incurred considerable financial loss. *N.G.R. SK 196662.*

The Mandale Sough which drained the mine and which was used as a pumpway for the water wheel and steam engine, was driven for over a mile along the Mandale Rake into the hillside. It was commenced in about 1797 and was still being extended after 1820. For some nine months of the year, crystal clear water issues from the portal. *N.G.R. SK 197661.*

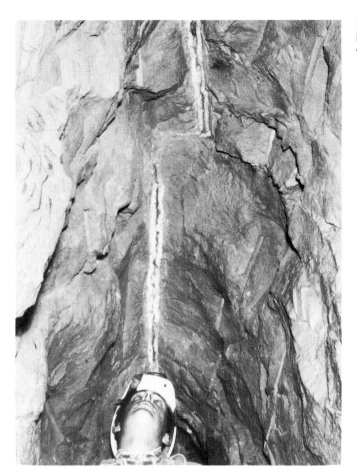

In a small working in the Good Luck Mine, at Via Gellia, there is to be seen a good example of faulted vein. Veins of narrow width such as this are known in Derbyshire as scrins.

In the Snake Mine, Hoptonwood, keyed stone stemples have been used on which to stack deads or rubbish over the passageways. Such stemples last indefinitely whereas timber eventually rots and it is the latter which constitute a real danger to the exploration of old mines.

Small tributers working for fluorspar in former lead mines frequently resort to using machinery which would not look out of place in a museum. Such machines, however, despite their appearance are often as efficient as modern methods. This small hand-operated crusher, found in a working near Matlock, obviously still fulfils the function for which it was originally designed.

On Masson Hill, Matlock, powerful fluorspar veins have been worked in recent times. Jugholes Mine is an example of this. Jugholes Cave, seen here, has at times been connected to an adit system driven into the hillside beneath this upper working.   *N.G.R. SK 280597.*

In contrast to the small machine illustrated overleaf, this large crushing circle, complete with iron-tyred crushing stone, is sited at Castleton on the Odin Mine. This once very productive mine had its main level or cartgate nearby, out of which the ore was drawn to be crushed and dressed on this site. *N.G.R. SK 135835.*

Derbyshire's most famous lead mine is undoubtedly Magpie, situated high on the uplands above the River Wye to which its sough is driven. The mine has witnessed several re-workings since it was originally opened in the eighteenth century. The engine-house last contained a 70″ Cornish engine which pumped water to sough level which meets the shaft 579′ below the collar. The last attempt to re-open the mine was in 1951 but the venture was abandoned in 1958. *N.G.R. SK 172682.*

In the outlying mining district of Crich stands the derelict engine-house of Old End Mine. In the course of working the Great Rake vein, the engine shaft reached a depth of over 150 fathoms, which in Derbyshire is considered a great depth. The shaft has now run in and the site is largely overgrown. The Fritchley Level near the village of the same name drains the mine to a depth of 70 fathoms. The portal of this level bears the date 1753.

N.G.R. SK 346558.

A well-known landmark on Eyam Edge is the stack and engine-house of New Engines Mine. It has the distinction of being the deepest in the county as the engine shaft reaches a depth of 182 fathoms. The pumping engine, installed in 1863, was built in Sheffield and was at work on the mine until it closed 21 years later. Magclough Sough was driven from the adjacent valley to drain the mine after the adventurers had become involved in a legal dispute with the proprietors of the deeper Stoke Sough.   *N.G.R. SK 224774.*

The Moot Hall, Wirksworth. Here is kept the dish given to the miners by Henry VIII in 1513 as a standard by which all dishes in the King's field had to comply. Mining was administered by a Barmaster and jury of miners in each Liberty. This jury, or Barmoot Court still meets at the Moot Hall occasionally, but now, due to lead mining having virtually ceased in the county, is regarded as a pleasant anachronism. *N.G.R. SK 288540.*

All that now remains of the celebrated Mill Close Mine at Darley Dale. A fine brick stack still stands amongst the contemporary buildings of a modern lead smelting works. Mill Close was, for many years, the most productive lead mine in Britain and had three Cornish engines at work on the site—affectionately known as 'Jumbo', 'Alice' and 'Baby'. The mine closed in 1939 after producing 430,000 tons of lead concentrates in the last 78 years of working. *N.G.R. SK 258624.*

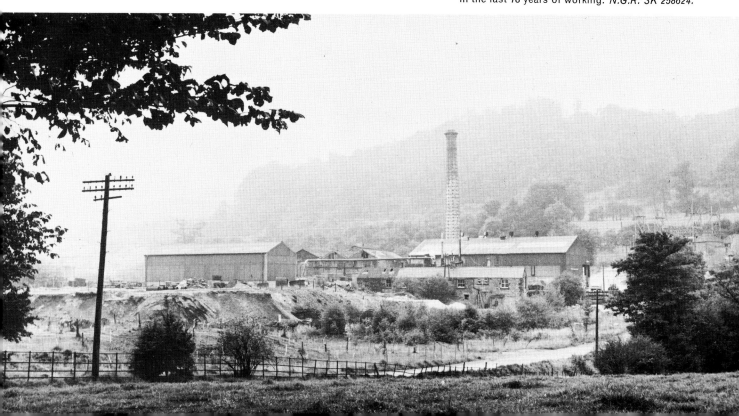

The Pennines

The southern Pennines having been dealt with separately under the heading of the Peak District, the region considered here embraces the area stretching north from Grassington near Skipton to Hadrian's Wall in Northumberland.

The predominant mineral mined throughout this extensive field was lead ore, accompanied further north by zinc blende in payable quantities. This was mined in the nineteenth century and the opening years of the twentieth.

The lead ore of the region was certainly known to the Romans who, as in other areas, were diligent developers of mineral wealth in the countries they dominated. Perhaps it is more than a coincidence that Hadrian's Wall was built at the very edge of the mineral field since no further important metal mines occur north of it until the Lowther Hills of Scotland are reached.

The whole mining field is of a relatively shallow nature, the majority of the ore deposits occurring above the horizons of the rivers which cut deep valleys throughout the area. Because of this, veins of lead ore were easily discovered and could be worked at points where they came to grass or "bassetted out" of the valley sides.

The usual method of working such veins was by a procedure known as hushing, whereby a dam was built above and periodically released, allowing the resultant rush of water to remove the rock and sub soil, thus exposing the vein. Any ore that was also removed in this way was collected at the bottom. Thus it can be seen that hushing was a cheap and easy way of working and over a period of years such hushes could attain considerable proportions. They can be seen particularly in Swaledale and Arkengarthdale and in the more northerly valleys of the Tees and Wear. The largest of all northern hushes is thought to be Coldberry Gutter, cutting through the divide between the valleys of Bow Lee and Hudeshope in Teesdale.

In areas which did not lend themselves to hushing, for instance on Grassington Moor, early workings were of the bell pit type. These were shallow shafts sunk for about 30′ on to the vein. This latter was worked in both directions at the shaft bottom until either the air became too foul or the workings too unstable. The shaft was then abandoned and a new one sunk further along. The Bycliffe vein on Grassington Moor was worked in this fashion, and remains of the bell pits can be seen today as grass filled hollows following the strike of the vein, strung out like beads on a string.

As mining technology advanced in the eighteenth century, the driving of tunnels into a vein complex for access came to be recognised as the best mode of working. These tunnels served a triple purpose. They formed an easy way of drawing out the veinstuff or bouse instead of winding it up deep shafts, they provided cheap drainage and they explored untested ground for new mineral deposits.

The larger of these tunnels became used as horse levels and are the principal feature of the North Pennine orefield. In time some of them, with their branches, reached great lengths, and in the Nenthead area of Alston Moor, which was the London Lead Company's chief centre of operations, the horse level networks are the most extensive in the British Isles. Such levels as these could only be driven with the backing of considerable capital and thus the mining companies of the area were large concerns able to lay out money on 'dead work' as it was known. Unlike the working of a vein, any shaft, winze, level or rise driven for access or development, afforded no direct return and hence was referred to as dead.

Quite a number of bold drainage schemes were undertaken, perhaps the most important being the Nent Force Level started in 1776. Driven between the Nent Force waterfall at Alston and the village of Nenthead, over a distance of nearly five miles, this solved the drainage problems of the area. It was constructed in part as an underground canal to aid transportation of materials whilst work was in progress. The Brewery Shaft on Rampgill Mine is the final shaft on the level, being equipped with water-driven compressors and supplying air to the furthermost parts of the workings. Unfortunately, the mouth of this level has now been buried beneath rubbish, but water is still drawn from it to supply a factory nearby. Other notable drainage systems include the Blackett Level in Allendale, never completed to its objective, the Allenheads Mine; the Eagle Level at Greenhow, also never completed and the Duke's Level on Grassington Moor, whose portal is to be found beside Hebden Gill.

Bouse from the vein was tipped through chutes into waggons waiting in the horse level and then trammed out of the mine. It was delivered into ore bins (bouse teems) and subsequently raked out of a hole in the bottom to be dressed. These bouse teems can often still be seen near the level mouths. The ore, after sorting, crushing and buddling was ready for smelting. In large concerns, this was frequently carried out at their own mill in the vicinity of the dressing floor.

These lead smelting mills are a common feature of the Pennine lead mining field and in the Swaledale area such mills still remain in a reasonable state of preservation. The Grinton Mill, for example, remains sufficiently intact for use today as a sheep dipping station, whilst further south near Pately Bridge, the Heathfield Mill, having one of the longest flues in the north (1¼ miles), has recently been converted into offices for an adjacent caravan site.

A number of museums, whose collections are either wholly or partly devoted to the region's lead mining, are worth a visit whilst one is in the vicinity. That of the Earby Mines Research Group is perhaps the most notable, whilst fine collections of tools and documents can also be seen at the Skipton and Bowes Museums.

This large block of native gritstone, known as the Panty Oon Stone, is a relic of thirteenth and fourteenth century lead mining on Greenhow Moor. Hollowed out to a depth of 24″ with an outlet to one side, it is thought that this was the lower part of an early ore crusher, used by the monks of Fountains Abbey to crush ore from their mines in the area. Its operation can be likened to that of a large pestle and mortar. Below the stone in Gill Beck is to be found the portal of the equally ancient Sam Oon Level.

N.G.R. SE 109645.

To denote ownership or title of a vein, boundary stones were sometimes used. The owners' initials or name of the group of adventurers were inscribed upon these and many such stones still remain on the intensively worked Grassington Moor. This well-dressed and cut stone denotes the boundary of the Duke of Devonshire's title. The Duke owned a large part of the moor and worked it to great advantage. *N.G.R. SE 031671.*

Remains of stone sleeper blocks at Yarnbury (Grassington) which secured the rails of a tramway constructed from Barrett's Mine to the dressing floor. *N.G.R. SE 015659.*

Winding and dressing on the Duke of Devonshire's mines on Grassington Moor was carried out by water power. The water was conducted from storage dams via a complex system of leats known as the Duke's Watercourse. This was some six miles long and much of it can be traced today as it winds about the 1150′ contour between the mines and dressing floors. *N.G.R. SE 019669.*

At Yarnbury, the portal of the incline level into Barrett's Mine can still be seen. It was used to allow access of horses into the workings and is still known locally as the "Pony Level". *N.G.R. SE 015659.*

Most Pennine lead smelting mills were equipped with long flues which conveyed the smoke and fume from the furnaces, often over long distances, to terminate in a chimney stack. With condensers added to the system, the fume could be precipitated with such efficiency that it could be cleaned out and sold as high purity lead. The flues of the Cupola Mill on Grassington Moor are ingeniously laid out. Built about 1780, the flue is divided, each branch incorporating a Stokoe condenser. Either branch could be shut off to facilitate cleaning the other.

N.G.R. (chimney) SE 029665.

▶

Cockhill Mill in winter. Situated on Brandstone Beck, this mill was served by two mines, Cockhill and Gillfield. The crosscuts and associated workings of these two mines had a total length of over eight miles. The mill was built about 1785 and contained a roasting house, ore hearths and a water wheel of 14′ diameter providing the power for operating the furnace bellows. Unfortunately, the fine masonry hoods over the furnaces collapsed some years ago. These were supported on cast iron columns which can still be clearly seen. The portal of Gillfield Level can be discerned below the road between the buildings. *N.G.R. SE 115648.*

A view of the Prosperous Mill, Greenhow Moor. The flue can be seen climbing the hill at the back of the ruins. This mill served the rich Prosperous, Providence and Stoney Groove Mines. *N.G.R. SE 124663.*

The Wonderful Level in Ashfoldside Valley, Greenhow Moor: the approach cutting to this level
is unusual in that it has been bridged by a drystone wall.　　　*N.G.R. SE 127662.*

Engine-houses are a rare sight in the Mid and North Pennines but such a house can be found at Cononley Mine high on the hills between Keighley and Skipton. The house has recently been restored by the Earby Mines Research Group. The engine here did not pump directly from the shaft but utilised flat rods with an angle bob at the shaft collar. The engine shaft is still to be seen, complete with rod track entry cutting built of rough masonry.   *N.G.R. SD 981461.*

To the north of Old Gang Smelt mill, beside Flincher Gill, is the Brandy Bottle Incline. This was sunk on to the Friarfold Vein about 1815 with the intention of hauling ore from that vein by means of a steam engine. The engine never materialised however, and the incline was used for the access of horses used for underground haulage in the mine. The incline and associated workings are connected with Old Gang Mine via a shale gate known as the Black Crosscut.

N.G.R. mouth NY 959020.

A typical north Pennine ore waggon photographed at the commencement of the Brandy Bottle vein off the incline. These waggons were of the end tipping kind and each held about 1 ton of bouse. They were linked together into a train which was pulled by a horse.

Gang Smelt Mill is a
cal example of a large scale
elting site in use during the
eteenth century.

N.G.R. NY 975005.

For the smelting of lead ore, peat was generally used, being easily obtained on the open moorland of the Pennines. As this had to be dried before use, open sided, thatched peat stores were built to allow air to permeate the turves. Peat was generally cut in June and considerable quantities were necessary for a year's working, particularly in busy mills such as Old Gang. The peat house here is 391′ long by 21′ wide and is a conspicuous landmark from the surrounding hills. *N.G.R. NY 973008.*

The Sir Francis Level was started in 1864 low down in the valley of Gunnerside Gill, and driven to the rich Friarfold vein to cut it in depth. On reaching the vein in 1877, a shaft was sunk to test the vein at an even greater depth. Winding and pumping in this shaft was accomplished by hydraulic engines which still remain *in situ*. These engines were supplied with a head of water by cast iron piping down a 43 fathom deep shaft from surface; the water then escaping down the adit level together with that which was pumped from the lowest workings. These deeper levels were not a success and the shaft was allowed to fill after only a matter of one year of working. The illustration shows the drum, crank, cylinder and feed pipes of the winding engine.   *N.G.R. mouth NY 940000.*

Connected to the Old Gang Mine, although driven from the adjacent Gunnerside Gill, was the Bunton or Bunting Level, the finely proportioned portal of which can be found higher up the Gill from that of the Sir Francis Level. As this level was driven directly on to the Old Rake Vein where it outcropped in the valley, evidence can be found of large hushing operations above the level mouth which were in use before underground mining commenced. These hushes are best seen from the opposite side of Gunnerside Gill.   *N.G.R. NY 942012.*

A small tributary of Gunnerside Gill enters the valley near its head and at the confluence of these two waters stand the ruins of Blakethwaite Mill. This smelting mill dealt with the ores from the nearby Blakethwaite, Lownathwaite and Swinnergill mines. The peat store is situated across the stream and in the mill itself, last worked in 1878, the furnace support columns remain, although the actual hearths have collapsed.

N.G.R. NY 938019.

Many extensive hushes are to be found in Arkengarthdale, near Reeth. Dodgson Hugh is one such impressive example, whilst further north lie the Hungry Hushes, so named because they are supposed to have missed the vein for which they were worked!

N.G.R. NY 995025.

Below Dodgson Hush lies the portal of Moulds Old Level, chief access to the Surrender Mines. Not only is the level very extensive but it also bore the reputation of being haunted, a belief which was applicable to many other horse levels within the area. Evidence of the great amount of underground work carried out here is seen by the existence of massive spoil heaps in the vicinity. *N.G.R. NY 997026.*

Arkengarthdale was exploited by the well-known C.B. Company whose name is still remembered locally and is depicted on the sign on a nearby inn. This company used large quantities of gunpowder for their mines some of which was stored in a powder magazine built in an isolated field near the road. Now used as a cattle shed, this attractive structure remains well preserved. *N.G.R. NY 999035.*

At the head of Weardale, to the south of the Stanhope to Alston road, stands the Killhope Mill, used for treating ore from the mine of the same name. The 40′ diameter steel water wheel was of the overshot type, water being carried to it from the rising moorland behind in launders supported on stone piers (now demolished). After turning the wheel, the water was conducted through a fine masonry tunnel to be re-used at the dressing floor below the mill. *N.G.R. NY 827429.*

One of the many horse level portals at Nenthead near Alston. The London Lead Company were responsible for the development of Alston Moor in this area, both underground and at surface. Indeed, Nenthead was itself built by the company to house its employees.

N.G.R. NY 781435.

In Rookhope valley, close beside the stream, stand the remains of the Rookhope Smelting Mill used to smelt ores from the Weardale mines. The mill dates from 1750 and the flue here, clearly shown on the one inch Ordnance Survey map, was nearly one and a half miles in length.

N.G.R. NY 925429.

The Nentsberry Haggs level, beside the Nenthead to Alston road is unusual in having a rectangular portal. The level provided access to a number of rich veins in the Cumberland section of Alston Moor and also ran beneath the county boundary into Northumberland having a total length of 6,930 yards. An ore waggon stands on rails just inside the gated portal (1971). Considerable scrap iron was obtained from the workings here when many of the rails were removed some time ago and unfortunately the whole length of the level is now no longer accessible due to the roof being blown in with explosives. *N.G.R. NY 766450.*

Much remains in the village of Nenthead to remind the visitor of its connections with the lead mining industry. Apart from the obvious mining remains such as levels, spoil heaps and shafts, the miner's reading room still stands and nearby a cast iron fountain erected by R. W. Bainbridge is to be seen. Bainbridge was the London Lead Co's chief agent in the area during the latter part of the nineteenth century.

N.G.R. NY 782437.

A view of Allenheads Mine in 1971. The bouse teems where the ore was tipped from the mine are in the centre. The mine office is to the left, whilst the stores, forge and ancillary buildings are in the background. The Fawside Level, main access to the mine, is in the retaining wall to the right of these. In 1971, the British Steel Corporation commenced sinking an incline for fluorspar on this site.   *N.G.R. NY 860454.*

The office at Allenheads Mine. Note the decorative window on the ground floor, the style of which is not typical of this area. This embellishment was due to it being the mine agent's office. A plaque, affixed to the upper storey wall (inset) reads: W.W.B. APRIL 11 1850. The mine was worked for many years by the Beaumont family with great success, finally closing in 1896 after producing 200,032 tons of lead concentrates in that century alone.

N.G.R. NY 860454.

Although horse inclines into mines are by no means uncommon in the Pennines, that at the Allenheads Mine had its portal almost on the village green—perhaps a unique feature in British metal mining. The entry cutting has railings round it whilst the tunnel itself descended corkscrew fashion into the workings. Locally known as the Horse Track, this incline has been sealed due to a reworking of the mine. *N.G.R. NY 861452.*

The gated portal of the Fawside Level, Allenheads Mine. An inscription on the dressed gritstone plaque above the arch appears to have been overlooked. Usually these bear a name and date. *N.G.R. NY 860454.*

A general view of Coalcleugh hamlet looking north. Coalcleugh Mine was an important Beaumont undertaking and worked powerful veins beneath the watershed. The earliest workings here were shafts sunk to the Low Coalcleugh Vein. Such a shaft, surrounded by a wall, appears in the centre of this illustration. Subsequent development entailed the driving of Coalcleugh Level which reached the High Coalcleugh Vein after 2500′. The hamlet of Coalcleugh is now virtually abandoned. *N.G.R. NY 801452.*

Looking towards Coalcleugh hamlet from the dressing floors at Barneycraig Mine. This dressing floor, within the Coalcleugh complex, lies below the Barneycraig Horse Level, driven in 1760 at a lower horizon to exploit the Whitewood and Barneycraig veins which proved exceedingly rich. Wooden rails were probably used in this level during its early working. The portal of the latter is to the right of the "shop" at the head of the dressing floors, the scene of recent fluorspar recovery operations. The modern concrete foundations on the site were erected at this time. *N.G.R. NY 803468.*

Grouped about the entrance to Blackburn Level, Rotherhope Fell, are the "shop", offices and forge. The latter is in good condition with a cobbled floor, hearth and workbenches still intact. A forge was to be found at most mines enabling maintenance of drill steels, picks, hammers and other items of mining equipment to be carried out on site. *N.G.R. NY 700428.*

The portal of the Backburn Level, main access to the Rotherhope Fell mine complex, is of large proportions. This level, laid out by John Smeaton in the eighteenth century, had a hydraulic pumping engine installed in it to pump water from the lower workings. It was last worked by the Vielle Montagne Zinc Company, a Belgium-based concern, from 1907-1914. Rotherhope Fell has produced over 60,000 tons of lead concentrates. *N.G.R. NY 700428.*

Lake District

The Lake District has been the scene of much mining activity, particularly around Coniston and Glencoynedale. The lead deposits of the latter area were worked in the celebrated Greenside Mine which closed as recently as 1962. To the north, the Caldbeck Fells have likewise been extensively worked, not only for lead and copper (the chief minerals of the region) but also for barytes and tungsten. Around Keswick, argentiferous galena, so named due to its high silver content, has been mined from Elizabethan times and in the nearby Barrowdale are to be found the remains of mines worked for plumbago or graphite (synonymous with the Cumberland pencil industry). Whilst the area can be expected to be rich in remains from these many workings, this is unfortunately not the case. As is well known, the Lake District is a region of great natural beauty and the policy has been to remove or obliterate any seemingly "ugly" scars from the landscape. In recent times this policy has been shown by levelling of much of the Greenside site and to a lesser degree, by reclamation work on Caldbeck Fells.

Whether one agrees with this or not, it can be argued that industrial archaeology is of great interest to certain members of the community, as is rock climbing and fell walking, and the destruction of such sites is to be regretted. However, the Coniston Copper Mines have not as yet been disturbed and remain, perhaps, the most interesting area for study. Covering some ten square miles of mountain and fell, these mines have been worked sporadically for nearly two thousand years. Shafts, levels, opencast workings, waterwheel pits and dressing floors are found in greatest numbers around the Red Dell Valley. The most important working was Bonsor Mine which was still interesting speculators in 1954 when an attempt was made to re-open the main horse level. Its greatest production was made during the nineteenth century and it was only abandoned then due to low copper prices making further working uneconomic.

A view of the Copper Mines valley from Cobbler's Hole Shaft. The buildings in the middle distance are all that remain of the extensive Red Dell Copper Works. *N.G.R. SD 290985.*

The important Bonsor Vein was worked through a number of levels and shafts. To the right of the large mass of Kennel Crag can be seen the incline up to the Bonsor and Fleming Levels. Considerable use was made of water power at the mines, the incline being worked by a 40′ diameter water wheel. In the foreground are the remains of a 50′ diameter water wheel pit at the site of Cobbler's Hole shaft. This shaft and wheel were used for raising ore from the deep eastern section of the mine which here reaches 205 fathoms below the horse level adit.

N.G.R. SD 288990.

The large leat which supplied water to the wheel at Cobbler's Hole shaft remains in excellent condition. The whole fell side beneath Kennel Crag contains many such watercourses.   *N.G.R. SD 288990.*

The ruins of the dressing plant buildings are found behind the Youth Hostel, once the manager's house at the Bonsor Mine. Crushing of the ore was carried out here by means of water wheels, the tail race tunnels of which can be seen in the foreground. *N.G.R. SD 287987.*

◀

The portal of the Bonsor Deep or Horse Level. This was cleaned out in 1954 when an unsuccessful attempt was made to re-open the mine.

N.G.R. SD 291986.

The Isle of Man

Mining in the Isle of Man was confined principally to that of lead, together with some zinc blende during part of the nineteenth century. The two great mines here, Foxdale and Laxey, had long and interesting histories until overwhelmed in the early 1890's by the worldwide fall in the price of lead consequent upon the incredible richness of the Broken Hill discovery in Australia. Both have left surface remains which are striking, in particular Laxey with its massive waterwheel which has survived to the present day and become a major Manx tourist asset.

The Lady Isabella wheel on the Laxey Mine is probably one of the most famous of Britain's industrial remains. Built in 1854, this massive $72\frac{1}{2}'$ pitch back wheel operated the pumps in the 220 fathom engine shaft some distance away. Water from a cistern on the nearby hillside was conveyed through an iron pipe and up through a masonry tower to feed the wheel via a wooden launder. In service, the wheel developed an estimated 200 horse power.

N.G.R. SC 431852.

To transfer the wheel's power to the rods in the shaft, flat rods were connected to the wheel crank and conducted over a substantial viaduct to an angle bob at the shaft collar. To support the flat rods on the viaduct, miniature bogie wheels running on rails were used. The Laxey mine finally ceased production in the 1920's.

N.G.R. (shaft) SC 432854.

Wanlockhead

Wanlockhead, set deep in the Lowther Hills, is not only distinctive in being the highest village in Scotland but during the seventeenth century was also noted as the centre of the lead mining industry north of the Border. It was referred to as "God's treasure house in Scotland". The area around the village and that of the neighbouring village of Leadhills, is a mass of mines and spoil heaps, as a glance at the Ordnance Survey map will confirm.

The important Straitsteps Vein was the first to be wrought here in or about 1680. This was later leased to the London Lead Company and after a brief period in other hands, was taken over in 1842 by the Duke of Buccleuch, together with the other mines in the area. Concurrently, a new smelting mill was built in the valley of Wanlock burn, much of this mill remaining today.

Reorganisation of the mines and smelt mill occurred in 1906 when the Wanlockhead Lead Mining Company took over the lease. Steam power, which had not been used since 1834, was utilised for mine drainage at this time. This period of re-working ended in 1934 due to heavy pumping costs and low lead prices whilst a brief revival in 1951 came to nothing.

Perhaps the most interesting relic of the former mining industry here is the beam pumping engine, erected some time in the early nineteenth century at the south end of the Straitsteps Mine at Meadowfoot. Power for this machine was derived from the alternate filling and emptying of a large water bucket fixed to the "indoor" side of the beam and working in a pit. The engine lifted water from the deeper workings of the mine into a drainage adit driven under Mennock Hass to terminate at Meadowfoot. This engine is now preserved as an ancient monument.

N.G.R. NS 870131

A view down the engine shaft on which the beam engine worked. Although the shaft is now sealed for safety, photography is still possible by utilising a remotely controlled camera. The timber partitions, pump rod and ladders are still visible. *N.G.R. NS 870131.*

A view of the lead smelting plant at Meadowfoot, erected during the time the mines were worked by the Duke of Buccleuch. The condensing flues at the rear are an unusual feature. Unlike those at Yorkshire mills these are lined with timber and are constructed in concentric circles which climb the side of Sowen Dod to end in a chimney. The flue is made of firebrick immediately it leaves the smelter, no doubt due to the heat from the nearby furnaces. *N.G.R. NS 855145.*

The rear of the smelting mill showing the exit tunnels connected to the flues. *N.G.R. NS 855145.*

The Bay Mine, in Whyte's **Cleugh**, was locally the first site on which a steam pumping engine was erected. The engine was built by William Symington in 1791 whose name is well known in connection with his work on steam navigation, notable the building of the tug "Charlotte Dundas" which was used on the Forth and Clyde Canal in 1801. *N.G.R. NS 867137.*

The portal and approach cutting to the main Day Level dating from the eighteenth century at Glencrieffe Mine. *N.G.R. NS 864135.*

Part of the flues from the smelting mill on Sowen Dod. The timber remains, which have clearly been morticed to receive the cross members, are highly impregnated with mineral and contain in excess of 3% lead. *N.G.R. NS 858144.*

Eire

Although not noted for metal mining, Ireland possesses a number of historic mines and a sprinkling of old mining sites that are of considerable interest. Both copper and lead have been mined, in scattered localities principally confined to the southern half of Eire. In terms of copper, Knockmahon on the coast of County Waterford was a deep old mine that featured prominently in the Swansea copper ore ticketings lists for very many years. The lodes here were abandoned in the 1880's, when the vast copper deposits of North and South America put paid to so many British mines, as were those at Allihies (otherwise Berehaven) Mines in the south western corner of Eire, in County Cork. Like Knockmahon, this too was partly worked under the sea and the remnants of these once great mines rival those of Cornwall in scenic interest. South of Dublin and the Wicklow Mountains, another large complex of copper veins was worked in the Vale of Avoca, in what was the oldest and most extensive mining venture in all Ireland. For years this formed the principal European source of pyritic ore, until displaced by the deposits in Spain. Lead has also been worked in the Wicklow Mountains, as well as in a variety of other scattered localities. At Silver Mines and elsewhere these veins have recently been re-opened on a large scale with very considerable success.

A view looking across the Vale of Avoca in County Wicklow, to the old Ballygahan and Ballymurtagh copper and pyrites mines. The river, and close beside it the road and railway to Arklow, are hidden by trees in the middle distance. The mill building on the right and the headframe (left) remain from the re-working here from 1959-62. The mouth of the Knight Tunnel—at 18′ square, the largest of its kind ever driven in any British mine—is seen as a dark spot visible in line with the electricity pylon. Old burrows on Upper Ballygahan rise in rows to the skyline.

O.S.I. Sheet 19 : 20 81.

An engine house on the old Ballymurtagh sett. From its size and position, this neat building contained a horizontal engine used for hauling waggons on the two inclines, one to the left down to the dressing floors and the railway to Arklow, the other in line with it to the right serving the higher part of the mine and Upper Ballygahan.

O.S.I. Sheet 19 : 19 18.

The main level into Tigroney, prominent against the bare yellow dumps which even today exude a sulphurous smell after periods of rain. The right hand set of rails lead to the ore bins, whilst the left go to the shed where a diesel locomotive used for haulage was stored. *O.S.I. Sheet 19 :20 81.*

The remains of two of the houses, for the pumping and whim engines at the Tankardstown section of Knockmahon copper mines lie immediately beside the coast road along the cliff tops from Tramore to Dungarran. The main shaft here goes down 212 fathoms below adit and the workings extend well over a quarter of a mile under the sea. The main period of working was from 1824 to the 1880's, seven steam engines being employed and six water wheels made use of, together with a work force of 800.   *O.S.I. Sheet 22 : 45 99.*

Tigroney Mine, on the eastern side of Avoca. This is the old pumping engine-house dating from the nineteenth century working of the mine, during which time it was owned by the Williams family of Scorrier, Cornwall. The 60″ Cornish engine was removed from this house in 1881. A fir tree—product of some seed blown by the wind or carried by a bird—now grows in the bob wall where the beam once rested. In the foreground are the ore bins that were used in the brief re-working period about 1960.   *O.S.I. Sheet 19 : 20 81.*

With the bare rocky mountain slope behind, this view of the Caminches section of Allihies Mine in the westernmost part of County Cork, is more reminiscent of nineteenth century mining in Spain than in Eire. Here, looking inland, one sees on the right the wide line of white boulders along the outcrop of one of Allihies' massive quartz lodes. *O.S.I. Sheet 24 : 58 45.*

A view of the Mountain section at Allihies Mine. The nearer engine-house stands on the edge of one of the deep gunnises (open stopes) which went down into the mine before shafts were sunk, and has partly collapsed into them. Up these smoke filtered from an underground whim engine working in the main level. This building housed a winding engine or perhaps the man engine that was installed at Allihies in the 1860's. Framed in the end wall is the Caminches engine house, about half a mile distant. *O.S.I. Sheet 24 : 58 45.*

The stack of the Ballycorus lead smelting works, on the summit of Ballycorus Hill (912′ O.D.) south of Dublin. Erected in the 1860's, this massive structure had a spiral of granite steps built into it to enable it to be used as a viewing tower. From its top there is a superb panorama of Dublin, the Bay and, to the south, the rolling Wicklow mountains. Ballycorus smelting house was owned by the Mining Company of Ireland and remained active until about 1890, chiefly treating ore from the company's mines near Glendalough.

O.S.I. Sheet 16 : 23 21.

Boiler-house, engine-house and stack at one of the several workings at the western end of the Silver Mines group, north east of Limerick. The layout and appearance of this big rotary engine are typically Cornish. The slope of Silver Mine Mountain is seen beyond, whilst the dressing plant of a major reworking of the mines lies a short distance away on the left.

O.S.I. Sheet 18 : 84 71.

Inclined against a heap of the hard veinstone quartz that it was installed to cope with, the remains of an ore crusher at Glendalough Mine, rusted but still in sufficiently good order to be driven. Bearing the imprint of a Welsh foundry, this is the sole remaining evidence of the once flourishing lead mines in this part of the Wicklows. *O.S.I. Sheet 16 : 08 96.*

INDEX